Beyond Coping Skills:

THE ULTIMATE TEENS'
WORKBOOK

Integrating CBT and DBT for Lasting
Emotional Regulation and Personal Growth

Richard Bass

2 FREE Bonuses!

Receive a **FREE** Planner for Kids and a copy of the Positive Discipline Playbook by scanning below!

Contents

Introduction

The greatest weapon against stress is our ability to choose one thought over another.

- William James

Research indicates that 60% of young people feel the pressure to succeed in life, and 39% have felt suicidal because of this overwhelming pressure (Mental Health Foundation, 2018). Parents and schoolteachers can sometimes be unaware of the stress their children and students are dealing with due to the reluctance of young people to open up and talk about the experiences they are going through.

As a result, workbooks for teenagers have gained popularity over the years because they provide young people with accurate information and appropriate psychological tools to learn how to cope with stress and anxiety. The value of workbooks is that they can guide teens on how to approach real-life situations using the latest psychotherapeutic techniques. As an added intervention, they can assist even the most reserved teen in working through their unpleasant thoughts and emotions.

Beyond Coping Skills: The Ultimate Teens' Workbook is a carefully researched and practical guide to prepare young people aged 13-19 years old for everyday stressful encounters.

By introducing two popular types of psychotherapy, cognitive behavioral therapy (CBT) and dialectical behavioral therapy (DBT), it seeks to teach them how to effectively manage triggers, challenge negative thinking, and respond proactively to stress.

How to Use This Workbook

The best part about this workbook is that the exercises can be self-administered at home. Over the course of five chapters, teens will be offered 50 different exercises that they can complete in any order, at their own pace. The exercises cover several themes related to everyday coping skills, such as:

- *How to identify unwanted thoughts, emotions, and behaviors (CBT).*
- *How to remain calm during highly stressful times and embrace the moment (DBT).*
- *How to become a proactive problem solver when faced with challenges (CBT).*
- *How to boost your self-esteem and learn to stand up for yourself (DBT).*

The purpose of these exercises is to support an ongoing practice of emotional regulation and stress management. Therefore, even after completing the exercises, teens are encouraged to repeat them over and over again, providing different responses each time. Even though the exercises are not designed to harm or trigger young people in any way, sensitive readers should take caution and consult a mental health professional before completing the workbook.

Chapter - 1

At-Home Self-Therapy With CBT and DBT

Nothing ever goes away until it has taught us what we need to know.

- Chödrön

What Is Psychotherapy?

Psychotherapy is a type of mental health treatment that can help you maintain a healthy state of mind. Even though it is recommended for children, teens, and adults who are experiencing psychological issues, like ongoing stress, anxiety, and depression, it is also suitable to practice when seeking to maintain overall wellbeing. In other words, you don't need to be going through emotional problems to benefit from psychotherapy.

You may be wondering how effective psychotherapy is in addressing mental health issues.

Research shows that 75% of people who practice psychotherapy show noticeable improvements in their overall wellbeing (American Psychiatric Association, 2019). Long-term practice of psychotherapy has been linked with positive brain changes, which can fight mental illness and reduce the dependency on medication to live a happy and fulfilling life!

To get the most out of psychotherapy, practitioners are often advised to display a sense of curiosity and openness to the process. This means being honest about what you are thinking and feeling and embracing those uncomfortable moments when strong emotions come up.

Medical doctors typically prescribe psychotherapy as a supplementary intervention to deal with mental health conditions. Before starting psychotherapy, it is common to first receive a medical diagnosis and prescription of medication, as part of a comprehensive treatment plan. Depending on what mental health problems you are treating, and what your personal preferences are, you can choose amongst a selection of different types of psychotherapies, such as:

- *behavior therapy*
- *art therapy*
- *exposure therapy*
- *group therapy*
- *mindfulness-based cognitive therapy*
- *cognitive behavioral therapy*
- *dialectical behavioral therapy*

For the purposes of this workbook, we will home in on the last two psychotherapies: cognitive behavioral therapy and dialectical behavioral therapy.

Cognitive Behavioral Therapy

Cognitive behavioral therapy (CBT) is a combination of cognitive therapy and behavior therapy. The aim of CBT is to increase your sense of self-awareness by helping you identify unwanted thoughts and emotions, or unproductive behaviors, and replacing them with more healthy and functional thoughts, emotions, and behaviors.

Once again, you don't need to have emotional problems to benefit from CBT. At a basic level, this form of therapy can be used to monitor the quality of your thoughts, emotions, and behavior. For example, it can help you detect unpleasant emotions before they grow bigger and cause internal or external conflict. With the CBT tools learned, you can process and safely release those unpleasant emotions without causing harm to yourself or others. At a more advanced level, CBT can help you deal with real-life problems, like feeling stressed about school demands, angry toward friends and family, or anxious about your future. Many of the problems you face in life begin as thoughts or strong emotions. CBT tools show you proactive ways of solving problems by adjusting how you think and feel toward the overwhelming situations you are confronted with in life.

Three Components of CBT

There are three main components of CBT that make this type of psychotherapy effective. Each component focuses on different aspects of the human psyche: thoughts, emotions, and behaviors. The general understanding is that thoughts affect emotions, which affect behaviors. Therefore, by improving how you think, you can ultimately improve the way you feel and behave during stressful situations.

Let us take a closer look at three components of CBT:

1. *Recognizing troubling thoughts and emotions*

The "cognitive" component of CBT helps you recognize thoughts and emotions that are negative or unproductive. Sometimes, if you aren't careful, you can make the mistake of believing that every thought or emotion is a true reflection of what is happening in front of you.

The reality is that some thoughts and emotions are sneaky and paint an inaccurate picture of what is happening or encourage you to make decisions you will later regret. It is therefore important to practice pausing and examining thoughts and emotions, so you can understand what you are thinking and feeling, and the appropriate actions to take.

2. Learning and implementing positive behaviors to replace unhealthy coping strategies

When you are feeling stressed or anxious, your natural human instincts will kick in, and you will turn to learned behaviors, also known as coping strategies. These coping strategies become the default approach to handling crises. Sometimes, the coping strategies implemented aren't healthy. Examples of these include isolating yourself, self-harming, internalizing your hurt feelings, or practicing destructive habits, like binge drinking, overeating, or procrastinating. CBT can help you learn effective ways of responding to stress that won't compromise your wellbeing or make the situation worse.

3. Embracing the present moment and focusing on the tasks at hand

The third component of CBT is mindful awareness, which refers to the practice of living in the moment. Mindful awareness is a skill that comes from the Eastern practice of mindfulness. Living in the moment is beneficial for your overall mental health because you are able to regulate your thoughts and emotions better. Instead of entering an endless cycle of overthinking or negative self-talk, you are able to concentrate on the activity happening in each moment and tap into your logical mind to solve problems that arise.

CBT exercises address one or all of the components listed above, depending on the specific instructions you are given. As you go through the exercises outlined in this workbook, pay attention to how your thoughts, emotions, and behaviors are related to each other. For instance, notice how changing your thoughts enables you to feel and behave differently.

Dialectical Behavioral Therapy

Dialectical behavioral therapy (DBT) falls under the umbrella of CBT; however, it provides different tools to manage unwanted thoughts, emotions, and behaviors. The main assumption of DBT is that the best way to cope with stress is to practice acceptance and embrace change. You must accept your current life circumstances for what they are, and wherever possible, make the necessary changes to reduce unpleasant feelings.

When DBT was first introduced in the 1970s by Dr. Marsha Linehan, it was prescribed to patients who were diagnosed with borderline personality disorder and struggled with suicidal thoughts and behaviors. As time went by, more clinical trials were performed on patients who were diagnosed with other mental health conditions, like post-traumatic stress disorder (PTSD), eating disorders, anxiety, and depression. DBT was found to be successful in treating these conditions as well.

You might be wondering how one form of therapy can treat so many conditions. If you closely study the conditions mentioned, you will find that they have one thing in common: They result from an inability to control intense, unpleasant emotions. DBT skills are effective in teaching how to regulate strong emotions and find healthier ways to cope.

Four DBT Skills

DBT is broken down into four skills: mindfulness, emotional regulation, distress tolerance, and interpersonal effectiveness. Each DBT therapy session focuses on deepening your understanding and confidence in practicing these skills. Below is a brief overview about what each skill entails:

1. *Mindfulness*

Mindfulness skills teach you how to calm the mind and refocus on the present moment during stressful situations. The aim is also to get you to move away from being too emotional or too logical during crises, but instead thinking with your wise mind (the balance between emotional and logical reasoning).

2. Emotional regulation

Emotional regulation skills teach you how to recognize and control strong emotions (particularly negative emotions that may cause you to act impulsively and take actions you may later regret). They also teach how to name, describe, and reflect on your emotions, so you get a better understanding of the emotional impact of each situation.

3. Distress tolerance

Distress tolerance skills teach you how to endure through hard times, without giving up. The purpose of these skills is to prepare you for stressful situations that may be ongoing, such as experiencing constant challenges at school or unending conflict with your family and friends. They teach you positive coping strategies to get you through these tough times, without turning to destructive habits.

4. Interpersonal effectiveness

Interpersonal effectiveness skills teach you how to improve the quality of your relationships by increasing your level of self-respect. When you respect yourself, you are able to set healthy boundaries, learn how to communicate messages thoughtfully (without hurting other people's feelings), and stand up for yourself.

DBT exercises address one or all of the skills listed above, depending on the specific instructions you are given, or skills you are practicing. As you go through the exercises outlined in this workbook, pay attention to the positive coping strategies introduced. Notice how similar or different they are from your current coping strategies.

Can You Become Your Own Therapist?

Traditionally, psychotherapies like CBT and DBT are administered by a licensed mental health doctor, like a counselor or psychologist. However, over the years, more research has been done, exploring ways in which therapy can be done at home-by yourself.

Self-therapy is a relatively new concept that refers to learning and practicing self-help strategies by yourself. It isn't a type or substitute for traditional therapeutic interventions, like booking sessions with a therapist. Instead, we can think of it as developing and implementing coping skills, inspired by what you would learn inside a therapy room.

The development of technology has contributed to the growth of self-therapy. Just scroll through your phone apps and count how many self-help apps you have already downloaded, or digital workbooks you have purchased. The fact that you can get access to psychological tools and exercises with the click of a button—without leaving your bedroom—was something unheard of a few decades ago.

Furthermore, in 2017, researchers investigated the effects of internet cognitive behavioral therapy (iCBT) in treating symptoms of depression. They analyzed data sourced from 13 studies, with over 3,800 participants in total, and found that between 5-11 sessions of iCBT were enough for participants to see noticeable improvements in their depression symptoms (Lockett, 2022).

So, can you become your own therapist? Well, not exactly. However, you can become your own cheerleader by prioritizing your mental health and exposing yourself to online resources, like this workbook, which can teach you age-appropriate psychological tools and strategies. With time and consistent practice, you can positively improve your mental health, at home, without having to visit a therapist.

Nevertheless, if you believe that practicing CBT or DBT the traditional way will benefit you, don't hesitate to find your nearest licensed mental health practitioner!

The first set of exercises you will learn involve recognizing and confronting unwanted thoughts and emotions.

Chapter - 2

Identifying Unwanted Thoughts and Emotions

Being a positive person doesn't mean you don't feel negative emotions. It means you have faith in your ability to get through tough situations, hope for better days, and the willingness to see beyond the drama.

- Leticia Rae

What Do CBT and DBT Teach About Unwanted Thoughts and Emotions?

Imagine that you are scrolling on social media and come across an image that triggers a disturbing thought, seemingly out of nowhere. The thought is so disturbing that you are left wondering if it is really what you think, or perhaps your mind is playing tricks on you. After a few moments, you notice feeling anxious and guilty about having such an unpleasant thought.

Has this ever happened to you? If so, you are one out of six million Americans who experience intrusive thoughts (Mikhail, 2023). You may have heard about #intrusivethoughts on platforms like TikTok, where there are plenty of viral videos exploring different ways that intrusive thoughts occur. We can define intrusive thoughts as unsettling ideas or mental images that arise suddenly.

Examples may include ideas related to harming yourself or others, thoughts about losing loved ones, or urges to make impulsive decisions. What makes intrusive thoughts distressing is that they sound like your own suggestions. If you are unaware that these types of thoughts exist, you may be convinced that you are a bad person.

Both CBT and DBT provide positive coping strategies to address intrusive thoughts. CBT suggests that recognizing intrusive thoughts is winning half of the battle. Simply take a moment to pause and notice what you are thinking. Look at the thought objectively, as if you were an outsider. This brief moment of pausing and observing (without formulating a story about the intrusive thought) can help to reduce anxiety and see the thought as simply that-just a thought.

DBT, on the other hand, provides emotional regulation and distress tolerance skills, which can help you manage intense emotions that arise when you get intrusive thoughts. Instead of focusing on the thought and what it might mean or reveal, you can tune into your body and work on returning to a state of calm, getting your breathing rate back to normal, and shifting your focus to positive thoughts and activities.

Exercises to Recognize and Replace Unpleasant Thoughts and Emotions

The exercises below combine both CBT and DBT strategies and skills to help you address and overcome intrusive thoughts.

EXERCISE 1
Tune Into Your Body

When you notice intrusive thoughts, it is a sign that you are not present in the moment. You may be overthinking, daydreaming, making comparisons, or visualizing something. To escape from the grip of your intrusive thoughts, shift your focus from the mental activity to the real-life activity occurring here and now.

Tuning into your body can help you do this! When you are paying attention to the tingles, sensations, and discomfort that you feel, your mind is positively distracted. Instead of making your intrusive thoughts bigger and more real in your mind, you can slowly minimize it by simply focusing on something else.

Plus, tuning into your body helps you become aware of intense emotions before they erupt. While they are growing inside of you, you can quickly respond with relaxation techniques, like deep breathing exercises, to regain control.

Here are instructions you can follow when tuning into your body:

- *Lie down on your bed facing the ceiling. Slightly spread your legs hip-distance apart and rest your arms along your sides. Take a few normal breaths and mentally prepare for the exercise.*

- *When you are ready, close your eyes and bring your attention to your head. Continue breathing normally while picturing your head. Ask yourself, "What am I thinking in my head?" Notice the spontaneous thoughts that emerge in your mind.*

- If your mind starts flooding you with thoughts, slow down the pace at which you move from one thought to another. Take your time looking at each thought but avoid forming any opinions or judgments. Just observe!

- Once the thoughts clear up, move to the next part of your body-neck and shoulders. Here, you will ask a slightly different question: "What am I feeling in my neck and shoulders?" Notice the spontaneous sensations you feel in this area. The sensations may be pleasurable or bring discomfort. Once again, simply observe without forming opinions or judgments.

- Continue the same sequence when tuning into your upper and lower back, chest, arms, stomach, and upper and lower legs. When assessing each area, ask yourself: "What am I feeling in this area?" Pay attention to the sensations that arise.

- When you have scanned your entire body, shift your focus back to breathing. Slowly regain your senses by wiggling your toes and moving your fingers, then open your eyes.

EXERCISE 2
Balance Your Inner and Outer Worlds

Would you describe yourself as someone who spends most of their time in their head or engaged in the activity happening around them? Did you know that being too immersed in your inner world or too immersed in your outer world can cause you to lose sight of what's happening in this moment?

For example, if you are browsing through social media and you are too immersed in the photos and videos you are viewing, you can miss out on physical and mental signs of exhaustion, anxiety, or intrusive thoughts. In other words, being too focused on the outer world makes it hard to assess what you are thinking or feeling.

However, the opposite is also true. If you browse through social media and you are too immersed in your thoughts and emotions, you can misinterpret what you are seeing. For instance, if you are feeling depressed at the time, every photo or video you watch can feel like a personal attack on who you are. You might scroll past a photo of a good-looking individual and make comparisons with yourself. This occurs because you are too invested in your inner world and unable to see and enjoy the outer world for what it truly is.

You might be wondering where your attention tends to naturally go: inner or outer world? Below is a checklist that will help you solve the mystery. When going through the checklist, tick the statements that apply to you *most of the time*.

Section A	
Most of the time, I find myself paying attention to:	**Place a tick if you agree**
racing thoughts going through my head	
my changing moods and feelings	
spontaneous urges to take action or say something	
vivid images, fantasies, and past memories	

Section B	
Most of the time, I find myself paying attention to:	**Place a tick if you agree**
the action taking place around me	
smells, noises, and interesting objects	
what people are doing or saying	
the sense of calm or chaos in my environment	

Check which "Section" totaled the most ticks. If you mostly agreed with Section A, then you are more attuned to your inner world. To achieve balance, you need to work on embracing the action and experiences happening within your environment.

Here a few activities you can practice to gently switch your focus from inner to outer world:

- Run your hands under cold water
- Get active-do a 10-minute cardio workout
- Call a friend over the phone and pay attention to every word they say
- Count how many objects are in the room

If you mostly agreed with Section B, then you are more attuned to what is happening in your outer world. To achieve balance, you need to work on noticing how certain actions or behaviors make you think or feel. Whenever you are engaged in a task, take a moment, and consider what thoughts or emotions are going through your mind.

Here are a few more activities that can gently switch your focus from outer to inner world:

- Write three things you are grateful for
- Once a day, take five minutes to breathe and check-in with yourself. Notice how you are feeling
- Write an appreciation letter to someone that has helped you recently
- After a long day, notice how your body is feeling. Are you anxious or relaxed? Thirsty or hungry? Tired or refreshed?

EXERCISE 3
Log Your Emotions

It is common to experience intense emotions whenever you get unwanted thoughts. The emotions are your body's way of sending vital information about your current mental and emotional state. The tendency for most teens is to get scared and push down these emotions whenever they arise. However, this coping strategy doesn't make the emotions go away permanently. Instead, they create havoc inside of you and start an ongoing, quiet battle.

It is therefore advised to embrace these unwanted emotions, so you can get acquainted with them. Treat them like you would a difficult friend whom you love, but sometimes gets on your nerves! Realize that your emotions aren't trying to hurt you, they simply want to bring your attention to how you are feeling at the moment.

Learning how to document your emotions is the first step to acceptance. Whenever you get an unwanted thought that triggers strong emotions, take a few seconds to pause and reflect on what emotions are coming up.

Write down exactly what you are feeling and details around the incident. Later, you will be able to use this information to learn which emotions you experience frequently, what situations trigger them, and what are your go-to coping behaviors. This information will help you manage unwanted thoughts and emotions better!

Below is a simple table you can fill out to log your emotions, on a daily or weekly basis.

Date:			
Time/s			
What is the best word to describe how you are feeling?			
What situation triggered this emotion?			
Did this emotion come suddenly or has it been ongoing?			
What were some of the body sensations that accompanied this emotion?			
What thoughts came into your mind when you felt this emotion?			
How did you react when you felt this emotion? Detail the specific actions you took.			

EXERCISE 4
Separating Facts From Opinion

Emotions are real because you can feel them. However, they aren't always an accurate representation of what's happening in reality. As raw and intense as they may be, emotions can sometimes show you what you want to see, rather than showing you what is actually occurring.

For example, your emotions can reaffirm your dislike for certain subjects at school, let's say geography. Whenever you step into geography class, you get an unpleasant thought about the teacher (too graphic to write down in this book) and feel angry that you have to sit there and participate. But just because you feel angry toward the teacher or subject, doesn't mean that geography is as awful as you make it out to be.

A useful skill to learn when reflecting on your emotions is to determine whether what you are feeling is a fact or opinion. A fact is something that you can prove with evidence, while an opinion is subjective and based on your beliefs, assumptions, emotions, or preferences (which aren't supported with facts).

Separating facts from opinions can help you manage strong, unwanted thoughts and emotions to ensure that you don't spend a lot of time dwelling on opinions. If you get an unwanted thought about your schoolteacher, for example, you can quickly categorize the thought under "fact" or "opinion" and decide to follow up (if it is a fact) or simply brush it off (if it is an opinion).

The exercise below will help you practice sorting emotional experiences between facts or opinions. Discuss your results with a close friend or family member, so you can get feedback.

Statement	Fact	Opinion
I had a bad day today.		
I don't get along with my older brother.		
I think my schoolteacher is rude.		
I'm unattractive.		
I don't look good with short hair.		
I get awkward in front of new people.		
I'm not working hard enough in school.		

My friend ignored my text. I think she is upset with me.		
I have a feeling my crush likes me back.		
If I don't act kind, I won't have friends.		

EXERCISE 5
Personifying Strong Emotions

Personification is the act of giving human characteristics to inanimate objects or experiences. You will see personification used a lot in cartoon shows, where trees and animals speak, and toys face real human problems. Personifying your emotions follows the same process; you assign each emotion, depending on its unique qualities, human characteristics.

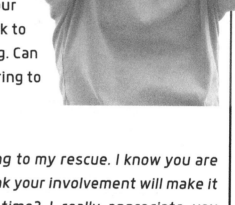

The purpose of this is to build a healthy relationship with your emotions (especially those intense ones), where you can talk to them like they were real friends and reach an understanding. Can you imagine noticing that you are feeling angry and whispering to yourself:

> *Hey, Anger, how are you? Thank you for coming to my rescue. I know you are trying to protect me in this situation, but I think your involvement will make it worse. Can you please come back another time? I really appreciate you looking out for me, but now isn't the right time.*

When you can build a relationship with your emotions, even the toughest ones, you will have better control over your reactions. In the following exercise, you will learn how to personify your strong emotions, focusing on one particular emotion of your choice.

1. *Pick any strong emotion of your choice, preferably one that you experience often. Describe how you feel whenever you are triggered by this feeling.*

_____

_____

_____

_____

_____

2. When is this emotion often triggered? Describe the types of situations that make you feel this way.

_____

_____

_____

_____

_____

3. *If the emotion were a human being, what would their personality be? Write down human traits and behaviors that match the emotion. For example, if anger were a person, they would be short-tempered, overprotective, fearless, sensitive to rejection, etc.*

_____

_____

_____

_____

_____

_____

4. *If you were friends with this emotion, what would your friendship look like? Mention different qualities about your relationship, such as how you communicate, how often you see each other, how you resolve conflict, the rules for your friendship, etc.*

_____

_____

_____

_____

_____

_____

_____

5. *Think of how you would respectfully greet and acknowledge the emotion whenever it arises within you? For instance, would you be casual and say, "What's good?" or firmer and say, "Hello, how can I help you?" Practice different greetings that represent the kind of relationship you have with the emotion.*

_____

_____

_____

_____

_____

6. *Lastly, when the emotion has arrived at an inappropriate time, how would you respectfully ask it to leave? Write down a few different ways you can show kindness while being firm with your request. For example, you might say, "Thank you for checking up on me, but I've got this situation handled. I'll see you another time!"*

EXERCISE 6
Become a Detective

What tends to make unwanted thoughts distressing is how extreme, violent, or exaggerated they can be. They paint a picture of a world that is unlike the one you live in, which makes you feel anxious. The last thing you might think to do is confront the thought, and judge for yourself whether it is true. However, doing this has been found to reduce anxiety and help you regain a sense of control over your mind.

Becoming a detective involves switching roles; stepping outside of your body and imagining that you have been called to investigate someone else's thoughts. This role switch enables you to confront unwanted thoughts from the perspective of an outsider and think logically about whether the thought is true.

Think about a recurring, unwanted thought that causes distress. Write it down below:

_____

_____

_____

_____

_____

_____

Like any good detective, you will need a list of questions to examine your unwanted thoughts. Go through each question below and answer as though you were an outsider investigating someone else's thoughts.

1. *Gain some clarity on what the thought is about. What exactly is being communicated?*

_____

_____

_____

_____

_____

2. *Is there a different point of view that the thought is overlooking? What vital information is missing?*

_____

_____

_____

_____

_____

_____

3. *Is there factual evidence to support the thought?*

_____

_____

_____

_____

_____

_____

4. *What are the long-term effects of thinking this way? How would this thought affect someone's life?*

_____

_____

_____

_____

_____

_____

5. *What advice would you give to someone who entertains this thought on a regular basis? What can they do to cope?*

_____

_____

_____

_____

_____

6. *Lastly, is there a fairer and more balanced way of framing this thought; one that considers both sides of the story?*

_____

_____

EXERCISE 7
Manage Your Urges

There are times when unwanted thoughts aren't visual or verbal but physical. Your thoughts may create an urge to behave in ways that are out of character or can get you in a lot of trouble. These urges may be subtle, mild, or strong; the more intense they feel, the more anxiety they cause. In your state of panic, you might think that if you don't follow through with the urges something bad is going to happen; however, that is not true.

Urges are strong impulses that come and go. When you don't follow through, the urges naturally become less and less intense until they eventually disappear. Your major challenge when experiencing urges is to simply ride them out and observe with curiosity. Remind yourself that there isn't anything for you to do, except patiently wait.

In some situations, your urges may feel very intense and unavoidable. Whenever you suspect that you are about to give into your urges, take three deep, slow breaths and answer the following questions honestly:

1. *Describe the urge you are experiencing.*

_____

_____

_____

2. Rate the urge on a scale of 1–10 (1 = subtle, 10 = very intense).

_____

_____

_____

_____

_____

3. Where do you feel the urge most strongly in your body? What physical sensations are you experiencing?

_____

_____

_____

_____

_____

_____

4. *What are the consequences of following through with the urge? List at least three consequences.*

_____

_____

_____

_____

_____

5. *Who will you hurt by following through with the urge? List at least three people (you can count yourself as one of the people affected).*

_____

_____

_____

_____

_____

_____

6. What can you do instead of following through with the urge? Write down three positive activities that can serve as distractions.

_____

_____

_____

_____

_____

7. What are the benefits of not following through with the urge? List at least three benefits.

_____

_____

_____

8. How can you reward yourself for not following through with the urge? Write down at least three meaningful activities to reward yourself with.

_____

_____

_____

_____

_____

9. What encouraging phrase or affirmation can you repeat to yourself to calm your mind and minimize the urge?

_____

_____

_____

_____

_____

_____

10. *Lastly, which close friend, family member, or doctor can you confide in about your urge? Write down a plan on when (date and time), where (location), and how you are going to start the discussion.*

_____

_____

_____

_____

_____

_____

EXERCISE 8
List of Pleasant Activities

Whenever you are confronted with unwanted thoughts or emotions, your first reaction may be to get rid of them. But how effective is this strategy? Ironically, the more you fight your thoughts or emotions, the stronger and more resilient they become. This is why DBT emphasizes creating more positive experiences, rather than fighting the single negative experience.

When you focus on positive ideas and activities, your positive thoughts and emotions multiply, and you can feel lighter and less anxious. Plus, since your mind is positively distracted, you won't feel overwhelmed by your unwanted thoughts or emotions. They may still be there in the background but certainly less noticeable.

Below is a fun checklist that you can turn to whenever you are feeling down and need pleasant activities to elevate your mood and distract you from unwanted thoughts. The challenge is to tick off as many activities as you can, within the space of a month. Once you have completed the checklist, select those activities you enjoyed the most and have another round.

Go for a walk	Plan a short-term goal	Doodle	Get a haircut
Create a vision board	Go on an ice cream date with a friend	Take a selfie	Buy a new item of clothing
Take a warm bath with essential oils	Visit a museum	Create a list of positive affirmations	Create a dance routine from scratch
Listen to your favorite music	Read a chapter from a novel	Take a nap	Clean out your closet
Watch a funny movie	Prepare your favorite meal	Write a gratitude letter to someone you care about	Plan a picnic or dinner party with friends
Get a relaxing massage	Perform a random act of kindness	Buy yourself flowers	Redecorate your bedroom

EXERCISE 9
Reappraise the Situation

Cognitive reappraisal is the ability to reframe how you look at a situation to reduce negative thoughts and emotions. It involves asking yourself questions that can gently adjust your perspective. For example, if you score a low grade on a test, you can see it as an opportunity to do better next time. This perspective ensures that you remain hopeful and motivated to correct your mistakes and apply more effort when studying for the following test.

There are five questions you can ask whenever re-evaluating a negative situation:

- *What lessons did I learn?*
- *What unexpected benefits occurred?*
- *What part of the situation are you grateful for?*
- *What progress have you made, big or small?*
- *What can you improve on next time?*

Think of three recent negative situations involving your home life, school life, and social life. For each scenario, answer the five questions outlined above, as best as you can.

Scenario 1: Home Life

_____

_____

_____

_____

_____

_____

_____

_____

Scenario 2: School Life

_____

_____

_____

_____

_____

_____

_____

_____

_____

_____

_____

_____

_____

_____

_____

EXERCISE 10
Practice ACCEPTS

Unwanted thoughts and emotions can send your body into shock. To prevent being overwhelmed with stress, it is important to distract your mind for a brief moment. Distracting your mind allows the intensity of your thoughts and emotions to lessen until they naturally fade away.

The DBT acronym ACCEPTS provides seven positive ways to distract yourself when you detect unwanted thoughts or emotions:

1. Activities

Complete an activity that requires concentration. Write down at least five practical activities you can try at home (e.g., reading, doing a crossword puzzle, completing a household chore, etc.)

_____

_____

_____

_____

_____

_____

2. Contributing

Perform a service to someone else, without asking for anything in return. Write down at least five acts of kindness that you can perform at home, school, or for friends (e.g., making a cup of coffee for your father, writing an appreciation note to your teacher, saying encouraging words to your friend, etc.)

_____

_____

_____

_____

_____

3. Comparisons

Put your current situation in perspective by comparing it to something more stressful you have experienced in the past. Write down at least three past situations that felt worse in comparison to what you are currently going through.

_____

_____

_____

4. Emotions

Perform an activity that will allow you to feel the opposite emotion of what you might be feeling right now. Write down at least three activities that can immediately brighten your day. Ensure the activities are positive and encourage lighter moods.

_____

_____

_____

_____

_____

5. Pushing away

Find ways to block out painful thoughts and emotions from your mind. For example, you can use delay tactics when confronted with your urges (tell yourself that you will address the urge in an hour, then reschedule again until they disappear). You can also use the personification technique and tell your emotions to leave. Write down a few more suggestions to push harmful thoughts and emotions away.

_____

_____

_____

_____

_____

6. *Thoughts*

Replace unwanted thoughts with pleasurable or productive thoughts. For example, when you are tempted to criticize yourself, you can think of three qualities that make you unique, progress you have made over the past few months, or tasks that you still need to complete before the day ends. Write down a few more pleasurable or productive thoughts that can become your go-to.

_____

_____

_____

_____

_____

7. Sensations

Engage your five senses through safe and positive activities. Challenge yourself to find activities involving sight, taste, touch, hearing, and smell (e.g., watching an episode of your favorite series, spending time outdoors if you enjoy the smell of nature, etc.) Write down a few more sensory suggestions below.

_____

_____

_____

_____

_____

Journal Prompts

Do you wish to learn more about where your unwanted thoughts and emotions come from? Here are some journal prompts that can help you dig deep and discover the underlying ideas or beliefs that trigger these thoughts and emotions. Take your time to respond thoughtfully to each prompt.

1. *When you get distracted, what are you usually thinking about?*

_____

_____

_____

_____

_____

_____

2. *What emotion do you experience most often? What thoughts does that emotion spark?*

_____

_____

_____

_____

_____

3. *When you are demotivated, what words or phrases do you often hear in your mind? Can you think back to where these words or phrases come from (e.g., you might have been called ugly names by a bully in kindergarten).*

_____

_____

_____

_____

_____

_____

4. *When you are afraid, what thoughts or images come to your mind? Where do these thoughts or images come from (e.g., you might see an angry image of your parents, which has stayed in your mind since you were a little child).*

_____

_____

_____

_____

_____

_____

5. *List five things that you worry about on a regular basis. Next to each worry, write down whether the situation is within your control. Reflect on how many things you worry about that aren't within your control.*

_____

_____

_____

_____

_____

6. *What situations instantly put you in a bad mood? Describe at least three situations and why they have such a negative impact on you.*

_____

_____

_____

_____

_____

7. Write down at least five things you regularly criticize about yourself, and the common nasty thoughts that are sparked in your mind. For each nasty thought, provide a positive perspective that allows you to think differently (e.g. "My nose is too big" would become "My nose is something that many people remember about me, which adds to my uniqueness").

_____

_____

_____

_____

_____

_____

Now that you feel more confident about managing unwanted thoughts and emotions, the next two important skills to learn are how to remain calm during stressful situations and embrace the present moment.

Chapter - 3

Remain Calm and Embrace the Moment

Rule number one is, don't sweat the small stuff. Rule number two is, it's all small stuff.

- Robert Eliot

The Importance of Regulating Your Nervous System

Your body's nervous system (responsible for your breathing, heart rate, sleep, movement, and stress response) is divided into two components: the sympathetic nervous system (SNS) and parasympathetic nervous system (PSNS). The SNS activates the fight-flight-freeze response and sends a rush of cortisol and adrenaline (stress hormones) flooding through your body. However, after a short while, the PSNS is supposed to kick in and ——

counteract stress, bringing your body back to its normal and relaxed state.

Have you noticed how uncomfortable you feel when stressed? A few physiological changes might occur, such as your heart starts beating louder and faster, your chest feels tighter, and your muscles become tense. This discomfort is a sign that your SNS is activated and preparing your body to fight or run away from potential danger.

In most cases, the stress signals continue to flow throughout your body until there is no longer a threat detected. Thereafter, the PSNS is activated, allowing you to relax and feel at ease. But what happens when the stress signals don't go away, and you spend several hours or even days feeling unbearable physical and emotional discomfort?

Teens who suffer from ongoing stress might experience difficulty regulating their nervous system. For instance, when they feel stressed, it can take several hours or days to return to a relaxed and balanced state. What this means is that their PSNS requires more support to kick in. Fortunately, both CBT and DBT provide skills and strategies to intentionally trigger the PSNS and induce a state of relaxation.

Relaxation and Mindfulness Exercises

The following exercises are safe to practice when you are feeling overwhelmed by stress and desire to regain control of your body.

EXERCISE 11
Create Space Between Your Thoughts

Thought diffusion is a technique that helps you create a safe distance between you and your thoughts. When this occurs, you are able to acknowledge what you are thinking without being overly attached. This technique is useful when you start overthinking. Instead of getting caught up in the details about a negative situation (past, present, or future), you can create space and let the thought come and go naturally.

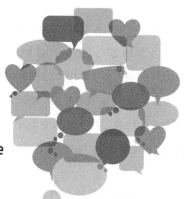

Here is a short meditation to help you practice thought diffusion:

Close your eyes and take three deep breaths. Imagine that you are relaxing on a quiet beach. You can hear the calming sound of waves and honking seagulls flying over your head. Pay attention to the thoughts entering your mind.

Imagine that every thought is written across the sand in front of you. You are able to look at the thought without feeling responsible to take action. Continue to observe the thought for as long as you like, then imagine a strong wind swooping past and clearing the writing on the sand. Now you are looking at smooth, white sand again. Wait until another thought passes your mind and repeat the process.

EXERCISE 12
Breathing Exercises

Breathing is one of the best ways to activate the parasympathetic nervous system and induce a state of relaxation. The aim, however, is to practice what is known as deep breathing, where you take longer, slower breaths to allow more oxygen to the brain. The basic sequence for deep breathing is inhaling through your nose, briefly holding your breath, then exhaling out of your mouth.

Below are different variations of deep breathing exercises that you can practice at home or school. Identify your favorite and continue practicing until you master them.

1. Count to 10

This simple breathing exercise can reduce stress while positively distracting you from unwanted thoughts or emotions. To practice, inhale through your nose and count from 0 to 10, then exhale slowly, counting backward from 10 to 0. Repeat this sequence several times. If counting to 10 feels uncomfortable, lower the count to 5.

2. Belly breathing

Belly breathing teaches you how to take fuller, deeper breaths. To practice, lie down on a flat surface, like a bed or patch of grass. Place one hand on your chest and another on your belly. Throughout the exercise, ensure the hand on your chest remains still (only the hand on your belly should be moving up and down). Inhale slowly and imagine you are filling your belly with air, then exhale out of your mouth and imagine you are emptying your stomach of air. You should notice your belly rising and falling with each breath.

3. Individual nostril breathing

Nostril breathing is a yoga breathing exercise that is good for the heart, lungs, and brain. Instead of inhaling through your nose and exhaling out of your mouth, you will inhale and exhale by changing nostrils. To start, block your left nostril and take a big inhale through your right nostril. While holding your breath, block your right nostril and exhale out of your left nostril. Continue alternating between the left and right nostril.

4. Mindful breathing

Mindful breathing refers to being aware of the quality of each breath. This exercise can help you end cycles of overthinking and focus on the present moment. To practice, complete the normal deep-breathing sequence. As you are breathing, notice different qualities of your breath, such as the pace (i.e., fast or slow), rhythm (i.e., consistent or irregular), temperature (i.e., hot or cold), and depth (i.e., shallow or deep). Take your time to observe each quality.

5. Focused breathing

Focused breathing is a type of meditative breathing exercise that encourages you to focus on a specific word in your mind. This word can be a desirable state or emotion you would like to feel. The objective is to imagine that you are inhaling and becoming one with the word, while exhaling and letting go of the opposite state or emotion. For example, you can inhale love and exhale anger, or inhale confidence and exhale self-doubt. Visualize the emotional transformation taking place throughout your body.

EXERCISE 13
Mindful Eating

One of the ways to reduce stress is to take a break from thinking too hard and embrace the present moment. Mindful eating is all about slowing down and enjoying every bite of food. It enables you to truly appreciate the flavors, textures, and smells of food. The aim is to find pleasure from consuming a meal, and gradually reverse the signs and symptoms of stress.

To practice mindful eating, pick a specific meal of the day where you get minimal interruptions (i.e., fewer people talking to you, less distractions around, etc.) Eat food as you normally would but do it 10 times slower and stop to take deep breaths in between each bite.

There are also a few observations you can make while eating, such as:

- *Consider where the food comes from, how it was produced, and who played a role in the preparation.*

- *Consider how the food looks, smells, tastes, feels on your tongue, and sounds while chewing.*

- Consider how many times you chew before swallowing.

- *Consider how your body feels after each bite. Assess how close you are to getting full.*

- Consider how your food choice affects your mind and body.

At the end of the meal, push the plate away and take a moment to express gratitude for the meal.

EXERCISE 14
Mindful Listening

It is common to react negatively when you make assumptions about what you think another person is saying. For example, if a friend were to say, "Hey, did you brush your hair today?" What would you think about their message? Would you take it at face value and see it as an innocent question, or would you assume they were hinting that your hair was untidy?

Mindful listening takes away the guesswork, so you don't have to overreact to what others are saying. Instead of assuming the worst or jumping to conclusions, you are encouraged to pay attention to every spoken and unspoken communication (through their words and body language) and seek to understand where they are coming from. To do this, you must take off your judgment hat and put on your curious hat.

The challenge of mindful listening is to hear what is being said without criticizing or forming your own opinion. Here are a few exercises you can practice during one-on-one conversations:

1. *Pause your own thoughts:*

Imagine that your mind was remote controlled. When you begin a conversation with someone else, press pause on your own thoughts and give the speaker your undivided attention. You can even take a deep breath at the start of the conversation to activate your focus.

2. Connect to how the other person is feeling:

While listening to the speaker, tune into the energy behind the words. What emotions can you sense being shared with you? Do you sense excitement, frustration, boredom, or kindness?

3. Summarize what you are hearing:

It is important to make sure that you are interpreting the speaker's messages correctly, and the only way to find out is to ask them directly. After they complete a thought and briefly pause, quickly summarize what you heard by saying "I hear you are saying..." or "I am sensing that you feel..." Allow them to confirm or clarify their message.

Mindful listening is also about checking in with yourself and sensing how a conversation makes you feel. Every few minutes, take a deep breath and tune into how you are feeling. You can even rate your level of comfortability on a scale of 0-10 (10 being very comfortable). As soon as your comfort levels drop below 5, it is a sign to either draw boundaries with the other person or walk away from the conversation. Remember, while it is good to make others feel free around you, it is equally important to feel safe around others too.

EXERCISE 15
Focused Meditation

When your mind is running wild and the world seems like it's spinning out of control, what you need is a few minutes by yourself to get grounded. The best way to describe being grounded is to imagine a tree with roots. The deeper your roots travel below the earth's surface, the more stable the tree will be, and shallow roots won't be able to keep the tree balanced.

Think of yourself as a tree with roots. When you spend most of the time lost in your thoughts, you tend to feel unstable and out of control. But when you take a few minutes to focus on the present moment, you regain a sense of control and are able to quieten your mind.

Focused meditation is a type of meditation that can help you get grounded. The aim is to find an object of focus in the room and give it all of your attention. Here are a few instructions to get started:

- *Set a timer for five minutes.*

- *Get yourself into a comfortable position and breathe normally.*

- *Find an object of focus in the room and intensely pay attention. For example, you can focus on a piece of furniture and study the shape, color, size, and other elements.*

- Alternatively, you can focus on a physical sensation, such as your breathing or a strong emotion you are picking up. Try to observe the sensation without getting distracted or forming opinions.

- When you get distracted, gently shift your focus back to the object or sensation.

- Continue paying attention to the object or sensation until the time is up.

EXERCISE 16
Visualization

Visualization is a type of relaxation technique that can help you lower stress and anxiety. The aim of visualization is to tap into your imagination and create mental images that resemble the desired experiences you would like to have. For example, when you are feeling anxious, you might visualize being at a quiet beach and listening to the sound of waves crashing on the shore. This mental image can be soothing to your brain and enable you to feel relaxed.

The visualization exercise below will help you combat anxiety by challenging you to imagine conquering a fear:

- *Close your eyes and take a few deep breaths.*

- *When you are ready, imagine a common situation that makes you fearful. This could be going to a party, speaking in front of a group of people, or studying for a subject you dislike.*

- *Play the situation in your mind from start to finish. For example, you might imagine the process of preparing a speech, starting with doing the research up until the final moment where you present in front of your class.*

- *Notice what kinds of emotions arise during each step of the process. For example, at first, you might feel stressed because you aren't sure what to speak about, but as you prepare the speech, the stress might turn to fear of embarrassing yourself in front of everybody.*

- Now use visualization to imagine overcoming your fear. Play the same situation in your mind, but this time imagine that you felt confident and motivated to face your fears. For example, you might imagine yourself getting excited when an upcoming speech is announced by your teacher and already planning what you will speak about.

- You might also imagine your teacher and classmates smiling and looking impressed while you deliver a powerful and entertaining speech. Turn every potential fear that the situation may cause into a positive experience that makes you feel good.

- Notice the difference in how you feel. What emotions arise within you? Do you feel more relaxed and confident? Has your stress lowered?

- Continue replacing every fear-triggering aspect of the situation with positive experiences. Embrace the pleasant emotions you feel while thinking about the situation. Convince yourself that this is how you are supposed to feel.

- When you are ready, take a deep breath and open your eyes. Whenever you are triggered with fear in the future, play back the positive experience in your mind.

EXERCISE 17
Remind Yourself About What Is Real

When your mind wanders to the past or future, you can get confused about what is real or imagined. You might wonder whether what you are thinking or feeling reflects your current situation or negative experiences that occurred in the past.

A simple grounding exercise that can help you embrace the present moment is to remind yourself about what is happening right now. Remember, anything that is real must be taking place in the present moment.

Look around you and confirm what you can see, hear, smell, touch, and taste. You can also remind yourself of the date, time, location, and task you are currently working on.

Here is an example of what you might say to shift your focus back to reality:

> *The date today is the 15th of July 2023. It is 2:30 in the afternoon. I am sitting on my bed, drinking tea. I have just come back from taking a walk. The house is quiet. I feel a slight chill on my back. My dog is sleeping on the floor.*

All of the statements above are reliable facts that enable you to recognize what is really happening in the moment. In the space provided below, write down different variations of how you might describe what is happening in the moment. Mention the date, time, location, current task, and sensory experience taking place.

EXERCISE 18
Find Your Happy Place

There will be times when reality feels too overwhelming to embrace, and your natural "flight" response kicks in. During that time, the only thing you can think of is escaping somewhere, so you don't have to face the present challenges.

Escaping can take on different forms, but most of the common strategies of escapism are unhealthy. For example, you might decide to mentally dissociate, disconnecting from your thoughts, feelings, and sense of identity. Or you might take the self-destructive route and escape by misusing substances or hanging around people who aren't positive influences.

If you are looking to take a break from reality, without disconnecting from your experience or harming yourself, you can retreat to your happy place. Think of the most peaceful place in the world. It could be a fictional location you read about in a book or a physical location you have visited before. Through a combination of visualization and meditation, you can visit this place in your mind, and stay for as long as you need to.

The beauty of finding your happy place is that you no longer need to leave your body or escape from friends and family to experience tranquility. The travel ticket is free, and you can visit as many times as you want every day. Plus, when you are feeling relaxed, you can step back into your reality and confidently face the challenges that seemed unbearable earlier on.

Below are simple instructions on how to find your happy place:

- Get into a comfortable position and close your eyes.

- Inhale through your nose for five slow counts, hold your breath for five counts, then exhale for another five slow counts.

- Notice how your body feels. Do you sense any physical tension; if so, where? Continue breathing deeply until you feel relaxed. If you get distracted, gently shift your focus back to breathing.

- When you are at ease, imagine that you are stepping into your happy place. Notice the setting, environment, and unique features there. Notice the lights, sounds, and smells around you.

- Notice how you feel as you immerse yourself into this environment. How different is your experience here than normal life? How do you express yourself when you are in your happy place; what do you do?

- Notice what thoughts come into your mind when you are in your happy place. Spend a few minutes embracing these thoughts. How different are these thoughts to the ones you have on a regular basis?

- Continue exploring your happy place, doing whatever feels natural to you. Every now and again, switch your focus to your breathing. Your deep breaths will ensure that you remain calm and at ease during your visit.

- When you are ready to come back to reality, take three deep breaths and open your eyes. Keep holding onto the pleasurable thoughts and emotions you felt while you were in your happy place.

EXERCISE 19
Write Your Thoughts Down

When your mind feels chaotic and you find it difficult to concentrate on one thought at a time, try writing them down on a piece of paper. This can help you keep track of your thoughts and relieve the pressure on your mind. Moreover, writing your thoughts down allows you to assess which ones are important and which aren't, so you can determine how much energy and attention to give each thought.

Have you ever written a list before? It can be a great way to organize your thoughts, boost your memory, and relieve anxiety. Your list can include reminders, important dates, or important tasks that you need to get done. It can also be a great tool to use when you are having recurring thoughts that don't seem to go away. Writing them down enables you to feel less pressure when constantly thinking about the situation.

Making a list is an easy exercise. All you need is a piece of paper or digital notepad. Number your thoughts as they come to your mind. If you like, you can organize the thoughts in order of priority. Below are examples of lists with categories as the main themes:

Category: Random thoughts

- I need to feed my pets.
- My haircut looks weird.
- Confirm the deadline for math submission.

Category: Friendships

- *Purchase Kevin a birthday present.*
- *Call Lucy later.*
- *Sleepover at Kate's house this Friday (ask Mom if I can go).*

Do you have any thoughts weighing heavy on your mind right now? In the space provided below, create your own themed lists to reduce pressure on your mind.

_____

_____

_____

_____

_____

_____

_____

_____

_____

EXERCISE 20
Set Daily Intentions

To prevent the build-up of stress, practice regularly checking in with yourself. A check-in is a few minutes spent noticing what you are thinking or feeling. You can have several of these quick check-ins a day, but the most important one is the morning check-in when you set daily intentions.

Intentions are positive thoughts you put out into the world about what you desire to experience during the day. They reflect the best possible outcomes you hope to achieve as you go about your normal daily routine. For example, you might set intentions about emotions you desire to feel, positive interactions you hope to have with people, or tasks you desire to accomplish before the day is complete.

Daily intentions help you focus on positive thoughts and feelings, which make it easier to have a generally positive outlook and attitude toward life. Even when you are faced with challenges at home or at school, your intentions are helpful reminders of the type of mood and energy you want to create and maintain throughout the day.

There are three questions to ask yourself when setting intentions every morning:

- *What do you care about?*

- *What small goal to hope to achieve?*

- *How do you desire to feel today?*

After you have considered these questions, write down a maximum of three intentions using the following format:

Today, I intend to [fill in the blank].

Here are a few examples:

- *Today, I intend to be patient with my parents.*

- *Today, I intend to get halfway through my geography project.*

- *Today, I intend to feel grateful about the small things.*

Now it's your turn! Create your own daily intentions on the lines provided below:

_____

_____

_____

_____

_____

_____

_____

_____

Journal Prompts

Do you wish to learn more about remaining calm and embracing the moment? Here are some journal prompts that can help you think of more ways to recognize stressful events and turn to the correct relaxation strategies. Take your time to respond thoughtfully to each prompt.

1. *What are the thoughts or emotions you tend to avoid? How often do these thoughts or emotions come up?*

_____

_____

_____

_____

_____

_____

2. *What relaxation exercises could help you feel more comfortable confronting distressing thoughts and emotions? How do you tend to feel when practicing these exercises?*

_____

_____

_____

3. *What are the early warning signs that you are feeling anxious? Write down at least five physical and emotional signs you can look out for.*

_____

_____

_____

_____

_____

4. *What positive action can you take whenever you detect signs of anxiety? Provide a few more relaxation exercises that can reverse the effects of anxiety (make sure they are different exercises than those mentioned in the first prompt).*

_____

_____

_____

_____

_____

_____

5. *When your mind races, and you feel overwhelmed by your thoughts, how do you normally react? Are there any ways of improving your reaction?*

_____

_____

_____

_____

_____

_____

6. *How comfortable are you with expressing intense thoughts and emotions? Think of a few positive strategies to share what you are going through, without harming yourself or others. Next to each strategy, write down what it would take for you to give it a try (e.g., you might try talking to a therapist if you struggle to manage your emotions on your own).*

_____

_____

_____

_____

7. *When do you feel most supported and safe? Write down a few situations that make you feel at ease and comfortable.*

_____

_____

_____

Now that you feel more confident about calming your mind and body, the next important skill to learn is how to become a proactive problem solver.

Chapter - 4

Become a Proactive Problem Solver

There's no use talking about the problem unless you talk about the solution.

- Betty Williams

What Is a Proactive Problem Solver?

There is no such thing as a problem-free teenage life. Every teen, no matter where they come from (whether they live in the best or worst neighborhoods) struggles with personal issues that make life more challenging. Studies show that teens experience similar levels of stress as adults. This means that the types of problems that young people face ———

nowadays are more complex than before and can severely impact their mental and physical health.

Perhaps you have felt like you are the only young person going through a hard time and that nobody else would understand the type of problems you are up against. Or maybe due to the lack of open communication at home or amongst your peers, you cannot open up and share how some of the stressful situations you have overcome recently have made you feel.

As a result, you may have developed a habit of concealing your issues and pretending as though nothing is wrong. In the short-term, this coping strategy can work, but it is destructive when practiced on an ongoing basis. When you hide issues and pretend that they don't exist, they pile up and cause a greater amount of stress and anxiety. Eventually, you may reach a stage where you can't hide the issues any longer because they have become too big to ignore. However, at that stage, finding appropriate solutions for those issues isn't easy.

Both CBT and DBT encourage you to become a proactive problem solver. This is someone who has the courage and mental focus to address problems as they arise, without waiting for them to pile up or become too big to ignore. A proactive problem solver is also someone who takes responsibility for their lives, and therefore believes that if something doesn't feel right, it is their job to find a solution.

You will hardly find a proactive problem solver pointing fingers at others. They would rather spend time thinking about what they can do right now to make the situation better. In other words, they focus on what they can control and forget about the rest. This is how a proactive problem solver is able to come up with temporary solutions to reduce stress and improve the quality of their life.

Relaxation and Mindfulness Exercises

The following exercises are safe to practice when you are feeling overwhelmed by stress and desire to regain control of your body.

Exercises to Improve Your Problem-Solving Skills

Are you tired of feeling out of control whenever you face unexpected challenges? Do you desire to learn how to become a proactive problem solver and take full ownership of your life? The following exercises will show you different ways of tackling problems to improve the way you brainstorm, strategize, and execute solutions for everyday life problems.

EXERCISE 21
Clarify the Problem

It is very difficult to tackle a problem that you aren't clear about. The first step of problem-solving is to figure out what the issue is, and how it affects you. Being able to do this can help you figure out the best possible solutions to resolve the issue.

Pretend that your problem is the headline of a news article. Using simple language, write out what the headline would say. Stick to only one sentence.

_____

_____

_____

_____

_____

_____

Next, pretend that you are summarizing the problem to a curious friend. Mention what, when, where, and how the problem occurs. Here's an example: "My parents are pressuring me to enroll for a summer sport at school that I don't want to play."

EXERCISE 22
40–20–10–5

Have you ever tried to explain a problem you were experiencing but ended up getting your thoughts entangled? You may struggle to articulate the problem in a way that others can understand. This is common, especially when you are feeling anxious; your thoughts escape you, or you forget the appropriate words.

Practicing describing your problem in different lengths, and with different levels of detail, can prepare you for those moments when you have only a few seconds to explain what the issue is.

The 40-20-10-5 exercise challenges you to explain a problem using 40 words, 20 words, 10 words, then only 5 words. The aim is to focus on the most important details as your word limit becomes less.

Think of a problem and use the 40-20-10-5 rule to explain it.

EXERCISE 23
An Outsider's Perspective

When defining the problem, it can be helpful to get some perspective. When you look at the problem from an outsider's point of view, you are able to see more than you would if you saw it from your own viewpoint.

Think about a recent problem you have experienced. Pretend that you are a spectator who happened to witness the problem taking place. Provide an unbiased, objective observation of what happened that day.

_____

_____

_____

_____

_____

_____

_____

_____

_____

EXERCISE 24
Identify Emotional Reasoning

How many times do you think about problems from an emotional point of view? You might worry about how a situation will make you look, or how it will cause other people to react toward you.

In psychology, this type of problem-solving is known as emotional reasoning. The benefit of emotional reasoning is that you are able to weigh the emotional impact of a situation. However, it isn't reliable when seeking to make sense of the actual problem, such as what is realistically happening at the moment.

Emotional reasoning sounds similar to this, "I don't feel confident in my body, so everyone must be judging me about it too." The mistake made here is confusing feelings with facts. Think about a time when you found yourself using emotional reasoning. What was happening at the time, and how did you define the problem?

_____

_____

_____

_____

_____

Consider how you might correct emotional reasoning in the future. Write down at least
three different strategies to challenge these types of thoughts and redefine the problem.

_____

_____

_____

_____

_____

_____

_____

EXERCISE 25
Journey Into the Future

When a problem is occurring in the present moment, it can consume your mind. You might fear that something bad is going to happen if the problem is not resolved right now. But what I have discovered about problems is that they usually get resolved over time.

When you feel overwhelmed by a challenge, it can be useful to journey into the future and imagine how it might get resolved. Focus on the best-case scenario rather than the worst-case scenario.

Think of an ongoing crisis that you cannot resolve on your own. This could be a situation involving multiple people, or one that requires skills and knowledge that you don't yet have. Journey into the future and imagine how this crisis might get resolved. Provide at least three variations of best-case scenarios.

_____

_____

_____

_____

_____

EXERCISE 26
Talk Like a Five Year Old

When was the last time you had a conversation with a five year old? Do you recall how they tend to structure sentences? A five year old doesn't have a lot of vocabulary or grammar to work with, which is why their sentences are often direct and simple. For example, when a five year old is upset with a friend, they might say, "I don't like the way you speak to me!"

Describing problems like a five year old helps you adopt the same direct and simple approach. The benefit of using this approach is that you can cut straight to the chase and express your main concerns. Think about a recent problem that you have overcome. Imagine how you would describe the problem to a five year old.

_____

_____

_____

_____

_____

_____

EXERCISE 27
Start With the Dumbest Idea First

The reason why brainstorming solutions can feel like a pain is because of the pressure you might put on yourself to come up with only brilliant ideas. Instead of writing down whatever comes to mind, you may become overly picky about your thoughts and feelings.

Starting with the dumbest ideas reduces the pressure of having to think of extraordinary solutions. The aim is to write down every small, irrational, or common solution you can think of. Don't hold any standards for the type or solutions you are supposed to come up with.

Take one of the problems mentioned above and brainstorm ideas, mentioning the smallest, irrational, and common solutions. Try not to think too hard about this. Write down whatever comes to mind.

_____

_____

_____

_____

_____

EXERCISE 28
What Would "X" Do?

There will be times when you struggle to come up with solutions because your mind is asleep, or you are faced with a problem that you haven't experienced before. When this occurs, you can think of what someone you admire would do in the same situation. This could be someone you know personally, or a TV, or media personality that you follow.

Pretend that someone you admire had a similar problem to one that you have already mentioned above. Ask yourself how they would solve the problem. What steps would they take to make the situation better? Write down the kinds of solutions they would come up with.

_____

_____

_____

_____

_____

_____

_____

EXERCISE 29
10x10x10 Matrix

If you want to improve on your ability to come up with solutions for problems, you can practice the 10x10x10 matrix. The purpose of this exercise is to help you come up with as many variations of a single idea, as possible. Thereafter, you can look back at the multiple variations and select the best option, or a combination of options.

PROBLEM
PROBLEM
SOLUTION
PROBLEM
PROBLEM

Identify an ongoing challenge you face at home. This could be a challenge related to your relationships with your parents or siblings, household chores, rules, and boundaries, etc. Come up with 10 big ideas on how you can resolve this challenge and write them down below:

_____

_____

_____

_____

_____

_____

For each idea above, come up with 10 more variations (i.e., each idea should have 10 options on how you can carry it out).

_____

_____

_____

_____

_____

_____

Now for the second set of variations, come up with 10 more variations (i.e., each variation from above should have 10 options on how you can carry it out).

_____

_____

_____

_____

_____

EXERCISE 30
Inner/Outer Circle

Eventually, you would have collected enough ideas to begin weighing the pros and cons for every potential solution. Remember that every idea, no matter how brilliant it may sound, will have benefits and limitations. Assessing these will help you determine how reliable each idea is.

A simple way to assess the benefits and limitations of your ideas is to create an inner and outer circle. Take out a clean sheet of white paper and draw a medium-sized circle at the center. Inside the circle, write down an idea you have come up with, as well as the direct pros and cons (benefits and limitations of the idea that personally affect you).

Draw another circle around the first one. This circle should be much larger in size. Inside the larger circle, write down all of the indirect pros and cons (benefits and limitations of the idea that affect people close to you).

Observe both circles and weigh the opportunity to consequence ratio (i.e., are there more benefits or limitations presented?). Figure out whether it is worth implementing this idea.

EXERCISE 31
Take Your Ideas to Court

When you are brainstorming solutions with other people and can't seem to agree on the best way forward, you can create a fake court and take each person's idea to trial. Every person in the group takes on the role of judge, and they get one opportunity to share their feedback about an idea.

As each judge speaks, everybody should note their argument (or there should be at least one person taking notes of every argument made). At the end, the arguments will be read aloud, and everyone can go through a process of eliminating ideas together. As a group, you must agree on the strongest and most convincing argument, which represents the idea that the majority of you have faith in.

EXERCISE 32
Start With the End in Mind

So, you have chosen a workable solution, now what? The next stage is to implement your solution in a strategic manner. The more time you plan on how you are going to implement your solution, the less likely you are to feel confused when you execute.

Starting with the end in mind is a traditional method of implementing solutions. The goal is to write down your desired outcome and chart your steps working backward. This method takes out a lot of the guesswork about what needs to be done, making the journey feel less unpredictable.

For example, if the desired outcome is to pass an upcoming test, there are a number of steps you will need to take in preparation for the outcome. Working backward, your list might include:

- *Desired outcome: Pass the upcoming test.*

- *Step 4: Practice using some past lessons a few weeks before the test.*

- *Step 3: Share notes and feedback with a close friend.*

- *Step 2: Go over study notes and raise queries with the teacher.*

- *Step 1: Create study notes.*

Create a fake dilemma and solution. Starting with the end in mind, write down the steps you need to take to achieve the desired outcome.

_____

_____

_____

_____

_____

_____

_____

_____

_____

_____

EXERCISE 33
Complete a Practice Run

Some solutions require you to take action. If you haven't already practiced the behavior before, you may feel a little out of place and nervous about implementing the solution. For example, someone who has never tried meditation before might feel apprehensive about practicing the technique.

To lower your defenses and get a feeling about what you can expect, schedule a time for having a practice run. The practice run should be as close to the actual exercise or behavior as possible. In other words, you should pretend that it is your first day of adopting the new practice.

Prepare for the actual day by rehearsing the steps or instructions and having the necessary tools to use. After you have successfully completed the practice run, provide feedback on how it went. Note areas that you can improve on next time.

EXERCISE 34
Create a Fictional Character

If implementing the solution makes you feel uncomfortable, imagine that you were a fictional character having the experience. Think about how this character would respond to new experiences that take them outside their comfort zone and adopt the same attitude.

When you sense the inner critic mocking or judging you for practicing the new experience, simply remind the inner critic that it isn't you who is engaging in the exercise or behavior, but instead, the fictional character. Eventually, you will feel comfortable implementing the exercise or behavior as yourself, without taking on a different persona.

Think about a new experience you are eager to try that can solve some of your problems. Create a fictional character that can help you display the confidence required to try this new experience. Write down a few beliefs and character traits they display that make them feel confident.

_____

_____

_____

_____

_____

_____

_____

_____

_____

_____

_____

_____

EXERCISE 35
Ask Yourself Questions

You won't know how effective your solution was unless you review the actions you took and give yourself feedback. The best way to know whether a solution succeeded or failed is to ask objective questions. The aim is to assess the execution of the solution and if you were able to achieve the desired outcome. This should not be used as an opportunity to criticize yourself or those who may have helped you. Try as much as possible to focus on the action you have taken.

Here are some questions to ask yourself:

1. *On a scale of 1–10 (10 being extremely satisfied), how satisfied were you with the results, after implementing your solution?*

2. What were you most proud of about the way you carried out the solution?

_____

_____

_____

_____

_____

3. What were you least proud of about the way you carried out the solution?

_____

_____

_____

_____

_____

4. How can you improve upon the steps or behaviors next time? Be specific about the areas that can be improved.

_____

_____

_____

_____

_____

5. Refer back to your brainstorming sheets of paper. What additional ideas could you implement to improve your current solution?

_____

_____

_____

_____

_____

6. Who did you reach out to for support during the execution? Were you satisfied with the support you received? What would you change or improve going forward?

_____

_____

_____

_____

_____

EXERCISE 36
Ask for Feedback

Another way to gain insight on the impact of your solutions is to ask for feedback. For many people, this can be a daunting exercise because, ultimately, nobody wants to face rejection. However, constructive feedback usually comes from someone you trust, who can offer you another perspective on the situation.

The purpose of asking for feedback is to assess how other people experience interacting with you. They tend to see qualities about you that you can't see on your own. Moreover, they may have interesting insights to share about your work, attitude, and behaviors.

One thing to remind yourself of before asking for feedback is to not take comments made as personal attacks on who you are. Remind yourself that the people you are turning to for advice are people who care about you. Their feedback isn't said to hurt you, but rather to build you up and help you become a better version of yourself!

The first step of asking for feedback is to identify people whom you trust. Think of at least three people (they can be friends, family, or professional people like teachers). Write down the names of each person and why you have chosen them in particular.

_____

_____

_____

_____

_____

_____

Next, you will need to send each person a set of questions. Below are examples of questions you can send. You are welcome to customize the questions according to the type of feedback you are looking for.

- What are three words that you feel describe me?

- What are my strengths?

- What are my weaknesses?

- How has my behavior improved over the past month?

- How has the quality of my work improved over the past month?

- How can I communicate with you more effectively?

- What do you believe I am particularly good at?

- What change would you like to see in me?

- Do you have suggestions on skills or exercises I can work on to improve?

- What encouraging words can you offer me right now?

● *Are there any positive behaviors I should continue doing?*

Collect the responses you get from each individual and look for similarities in what they say. Notice how many times the same points are mentioned and write them down. Those should be the highlights of your feedback. Schedule enough time to tackle each improvement (i.e., three months, six months, or a year). Implement the advice you have been given and experiment with new solutions. After making the necessary changes, reach out to the same people for a follow-up feedback session.

EXERCISE 37
Stop-Start-Continue

After completing a project that involves multiple steps, review your progress by practicing the stop-start-continue exercise. Schedule a day when you can sit alone and reflect on the project outcomes. Think back to each stage of the project and the various tasks you had to complete.

Go through each task and ask yourself, "Do I need to stop, start, or continue this task?" Tasks that were unsuccessful due to being time wasters must be stopped. Tasks that were planned but never implemented can be started on future projects. Tasks that were successful and brought the desired results must be continued.

You can also sort the project tasks into three columns, as illustrated below:

Stop	Start	Continue

EXERCISE 38
Reflect on Funny Moments

You won't always get the implementation right on the first or second try. Solving problems isn't about reaching perfection but learning more about yourself as you take responsibility for your life. There will be a lot of trial and error involved when seeking the right solutions, which means that you will most likely make a lot of mistakes.

Instead of beating yourself up when you try something and fail, learn to find the humor in the situation. Laugh about those random or awkward moments and see them as a part of the learning process.

Can you recall funny moments when you have stepped outside of your comfort zone and tried something new? Write a few of them down below.

_____

_____

_____

_____

_____

_____

Journal Prompts

Do you wish to learn more about proactive problem-solving? Here are some journal prompts that can help you think of more ways to confront the challenges you are faced with at home and school. Take your time to respond thoughtfully to each prompt.

1. *Think about a problem that your family is faced with. Define the problem using the 40–20–10–5 rule.*

_____

_____

_____

_____

_____

_____

2. *Next, use the 10x10x10 matrix method to come up with potential solutions on how you can solve the problem together. Call a family meeting and present your ideas.*

_____

_____

_____

_____

_____

_____

3. *Think about a problem that you are faced with at school. Describe the problem from an outsider's perspective.*

_____

_____

_____

_____

_____

_____

4. *Next, think about what someone you admire would do if they were in your situation. Write down their advice.*

_____

_____

_____

_____

_____

_____

5. *Think about a short-term goal that you want to accomplish within six months. Start with the end in mind and write out each step that you need to follow to achieve your goal.*

_____

_____

_____

_____

_____

6. *Think about an upcoming event or task that is giving you anxiety. Complete a practice run of the behaviors you will need to perform when the time arrives. Share feedback on how the practice run went and areas you can improve.*

_____

_____

_____

_____

_____

7. *Approach a schoolteacher and ask for feedback on your performance. Think of 5–10 questions that you can ask about your behavior, productivity, and quality of work and write them down below.*

_____

_____

_____

_____

_____

Now that you feel more confident about solving your own problems, the final important skill to learn is how to build a healthy self-esteem.

Chapter - 5

Give Yourself a Self-Esteem Boost

One of the most courageous things you can do is identify yourself, know who you are, what you believe in, and where you want to go

- Sheila Murray Bethel

How Can Improving Your Self-Esteem Reduce Stress and Anxiety?

As you experience different life situations, it is normal to go from feeling good about yourself to doubting your capabilities. Sometimes, life can knock you down with unpleasant circumstances that leave you feeling unmotivated and disappointed with yourself.

Self-esteem can be defined as the opinion you hold about yourself. This opinion can be positive, negative, or indifferent. Your self-esteem tends to increase whenever you feel a sense of accomplishment or positive about life in general. It tends to decrease whenever you experience failure, self-doubt, or feel like you need to hold yourself to extremely high standards.

The constant rise and drop in self-esteem can become overwhelming on your mind and body. Can you imagine how tired you would feel if one minute you felt confident, and a few hours later you felt displeased with yourself? This type of fluctuation can lead to mood swings, anxiety, and depression, or cause you to sabotage healthy relationships with others.

Both CBT and DBT can help you stabilize your self-esteem by teaching you coping strategies to practice whenever you feel doubtful or judgmental of yourself. CBT encourages you to think about the impact of your thoughts and emotions on your self-esteem and replace unwanted thoughts and feelings with positive self-talk and empowering beliefs that can help you build confidence. DBT, on the other hand, teaches you how to radically accept your life for what it is and find meaning in the setbacks.

Exercises to Encourage a Healthy Self-Esteem

The following exercises can be practiced on a regular basis to promote a healthy self-esteem. When you are going through these exercises, remember that no human being or situation will ever be perfect, and you are always doing the best you can!

EXERCISE 39
Improve Your Self-Talk

Your self-talk refers to the tone and language you use when having internal dialogues with yourself. You often hear about the inner critic. Well, that is a metaphor for the negative self-talk that sometimes occurs in your mind. The tone and language of the inner critic can be so strong and violent that you can hear an angry or mocking voice. The only way to lower the volume of this voice is to cultivate positive self-talk through positive thinking.

Positive self-talk refers to speaking to yourself in a gentle and compassionate tone, using encouraging language. Unlike the inner critic, the inner advocate voice is encouraging and focuses on what you are doing right, instead of what you are doing wrong. Think of that kind schoolteacher from kindergarten or your grandma who always finds something good in every situation. The inner advocate speaks to you in the same warm tone and positive language.

You can improve your self-talk by learning two techniques: how to pause negative self-talk and reframe those self-critical thoughts. The first technique is straightforward. Whenever you catch a thought that puts you down, makes you feel small, or feels unloving, immediately stop everything you are doing. Step away from the task you were busy with, put down your phone, and freeze. You may even need to yell, "Stop!" or "That's enough!" to get your mind's attention.

Take a few deep breaths and enjoy the stillness in the room. When you are feeling calm, write the self-critical thought down somewhere, so you can keep track of your negative thoughts.

Thereafter, activate the inner advocate and reframe the thought to sound gentle and reassuring. Don't change the facts, simply change how you phrase the thought to promote a more positive outlook.

Practice reframing negative self-talk by completing the table below. The first row has been completed for you.

Inner critic	Inner Advocate
e.g., You are so loud, it's embarrassing!	You get really excited when you are talking about something you care about. Be mindful of your volume during those moments.
Your fashion sense is so outdated.	
You will be single for the rest of your life.	
You act weird whenever you go out.	
Don't raise your hand in class. Everybody will judge you.	
You aren't a typical A-student.	

Your friends have better parents than you.	
Why are you always broke?	
You probably won't go to college.	

EXERCISE 40
10 Things I Love About Me

If I asked you to list both positive and negative qualities about yourself, which list do you think would be longer?

Science shows that the human brain is wired to remember negative events more vividly than positive events. Moreover, the body tends to have a stronger emotional reaction to negative events than positive events. In essence, this means that it is more natural for you to think negatively–and that you need to invest more effort to think and react positively.

One of the ways to practice thinking positively is to get into the habit of focusing on what you love about yourself, instead of constantly looking for qualities you dislike or seek to change.

At first, you might struggle to create a list of qualities you love. Your brain may need time to adjust its focus and memorize positive details about you. However, as time goes on, you will find that it is easier to think of positive qualities from the top of your mind.

To practice noticing what you love about yourself, start by listing:

- *2 compliments you regularly receive from others.*

- *2 unique facial or body features that enhance your appearance.*

- *2 skills or talents that come naturally to you.*

- *2 ways you show kindness to others.*

2 achievements you are proud of.

_____

_____

_____

_____

_____

_____

_____

_____

In total, you should have a list of 10 qualities that you love about yourself. The next time you complete this exercise, choose a different set of qualities.

EXERCISE 41
Reflect on the Battles Won

When you are in trouble or under significant stress, the inner critic can sometimes bring up worst-case scenarios. If you aren't careful, you might believe those thoughts and end up in a panic.

To maintain confidence during difficult times, it is important to remind yourself of past battles you have won. There are certain situations from months or years ago that seemed impossible to overcome at the time until you took action or made different choices. Reminding yourself of those battles can provide a source of motivation and courage when new and overwhelming challenges arise.

In the space provided below, reflect on three past battles you won. For each battle, clearly specify what actions or choices you made to positively turn the situation around.

Scenario 1: Home Life

_____

_____

_____

_____

_____

Scenario 2: School Life

Scenario 3: Social Life

_____

_____

_____

_____

_____

_____

_____

EXERCISE 42
Gratitude Letter to Your Hero

To be who you are today, there have been a number of people who
have played small and major roles in your life. These people may
have supported you physically, emotionally, or academically over
the many years.

Write a gratitude letter to someone who has been a positive influence in your life, someone
whom you respect and hope to become like one day. In the letter, explain why you are
grateful for their presence in your life and mention at least three qualities you admire
about them and hope to adopt. You can choose to either keep or send the letter to the
recipient.

_____

_____

_____

_____

_____

_____

EXERCISE 43
Gratitude Letter to Your Younger Self

Somebody else who is a real champion and deserves praise for surviving some of the lowest points in your life is your younger self. Even though you didn't have the psychological skills to understand what was happening around you as a child, you demonstrated mental strength and made it through the difficult times.

Write a letter to a younger version of you. Pick an age or age range when you faced the toughest battles. For example, you may have fallen ill, experienced bullying, or witnessed conflict at home. In the letter, explain why you are proud of that younger self and mention some strengths they displayed.

_____

_____

_____

_____

_____

_____

_____

EXERCISE 44
Discover Your Core Values

Core values are the foundational qualities, experiences, or principles that you live by. They help you structure life according to what matters most to you. Having core values can boost your self-esteem because they enable you to express your needs and set healthy boundaries with others.

You may already have an idea of the things you value but may not know how to articulate them. The following exercise will help you identify and describe your core values.

The first step is to brainstorm potential values. Go through the table below and circle all of the values that you connect with.

Patience	Creativity	Family	Wealth creation
Achievement	Respect	Community	Security
Spirituality	Friendship	Risk-taking	Adventure
Balance	Self-confidence	Kindness	Independence
Freedom	Acceptance	Integrity	Socializing

Continuous learning	Personal development	Generosity	Health and wellbeing
Autonomy	Beauty	Equality	Sustainability
Leadership	Commitment	Minimalism	Flexibility

Next, assign similar values under groups and give each group a theme or category name. For example, friendship, socializing, and community are similar values that fall under the category name: Social life.

Social Life			
Friendship			
Socializing			
Community			

The category names represent those qualities or experiences that matter most to you. Reorganize the category names from most to least important. Next to each name, give an example of how you would honor or make time for the value in real life.

For example:

Social life: Text close friends once a day. Attend a social event or meetup at least once a month.

_____

_____

_____

_____

_____

_____

_____

EXERCISE 45
Learning From Your Mistakes

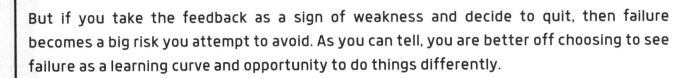

Society has made us believe that failure is a sign of weakness, and we should all aim to be perfect. This warped idea has made many generations of people live with the fear of failure. But what exactly is failure, and how can you positively reframe how you look at it?

Failure occurs when your goals don't go according to plan due to mistakes made along the way. The mistakes are feedback that something is wrong and needs to be fixed or changed. If you take the feedback and make the necessary changes, you can turn failure into an opportunity to learn and grow.

But if you take the feedback as a sign of weakness and decide to quit, then failure becomes a big risk you attempt to avoid. As you can tell, you are better off choosing to see failure as a learning curve and opportunity to do things differently.

Think back to a time in your life when you made a big mistake. From the story, identity the following:

- *2 new things you learned about yourself.*

- *2 new things you learned about life in general.*

- *2 new things you learned about mental health.*

- *2 new things you learned about relationships with people.*

EXERCISE 46
Create Boundaries

To feel confident in who you are, you must feel respected by those closest to you. Being respected by friends and family reflects your sense of worth; it shows that you are special and what you have to say matters.

Nevertheless, to earn respect from others, you must first respect yourself. It is true what they say: You teach people how to treat you. A great way to build self-respect is to hold others accountable to your boundaries.

We can define boundaries as the limits that separate who you are from who others are. These limits protect you from investing too much time, energy, and effort into your relationships at the expense of your wellbeing.

There are different types of boundaries that you can create, such as:

1. *Physical boundaries: Limits based on the kinds of physical touch or physical space/distance you are comfortable with from friends, family, and strangers. An example of a physical boundary is strictly giving high-fives to friends and acquaintances.*

2. *Emotional boundaries: Limits based on how you desire people to respond to your needs, listen to your stories, or validate your feelings. An example of an emotional boundary is asking not to be interrupted while you are speaking.*

3. *Mental boundaries:* *Limits based on how you would like others to respect your thoughts, opinions, and beliefs, as well as how you prefer to resolve conflict. An example of a mental boundary is refusing to continue engaging in a conversation when someone insults you.*

You can communicate boundaries with a simple sentence: "I feel [emotion]; I need [boundary]." For example, if you are debating a topic with friends, and the conversation becomes aggressive, you can say, "I feel overwhelmed by the way this conversation is going. I need to step away for a few minutes and take a moment to breathe."

Another example is when your family members violate your personal space at home. You might set a boundary by saying "I feel disrespected when you enter my room without my permission. I need you to knock when the door is closed and wait for me to open."

Now it's your turn. Think of physical, emotional, and mental boundaries you can set with loved ones. Use the sentences "I feel...," and "I need..." to create boundary statements.

_____

_____

_____

_____

_____

_____

EXERCISE 47
Positive Conflict Resolution

It is common to have disagreements with friends and family over needs and expectations. However, these disagreements shouldn't threaten the bond you share. When you are upset and feel misunderstood, the hardest thing is sharing with others how you truly feel. It is much easier to yell, hurl insults, or give the silent treatment than being vulnerable and expressing your needs.

Positive conflict resolution is about having the courage to address your concerns and openly share your thoughts and feelings. The hope is that by being vulnerable, you are able to have a constructive conversation about what you need moving forward.

There are four steps to positive conflict resolution:

1. *Describe the situation objectively (stick to facts only).*

2. *Express how it makes you feel.*

3. *Specify what you need, or would like to see happening, moving forward.*

4. *Outline the consequences if nothing changes.*

Below is an example of how you might practice these steps in a real conflict:

- **Describe:** Last night, I struggled to study because the music coming from your room was very loud.

- **Express:** I felt angry because it threw me off the schedule I had planned.

- **Specify:** In future, can you please put on your headset in the evenings to avoid disturbing my study time?

- **Outline:** If nothing changes, I will have to rethink offering my assistance with your own homework tasks.

Now it is your turn. Think about a common issue that you tend to fight about at home or school. Write down how you would resolve the conflict using the four steps.

_____

_____

_____

_____

_____

_____

_____

_____

EXERCISE 48
Rating the Intensity of a Crisis

Not every situation requires your active involvement. There are some situations, like overhearing people gossiping about you, that seem urgent but aren't important at all. The reason these situations aren't important is because they don't affect your livelihood. For example, what other people say about you doesn't change how you choose to live your life.

However, there are also some situations that seem urgent and are extremely important, such as someone threatening to hurt you. The reason these situations are extremely important is because they impact your sense of safety and overall wellbeing. For example, not only can a threat to physically harm you be true, but it can also make you afraid to step outside of your house or go to school.

Rating the intensity of crises helps you assess how much time and energy to give a situation.

On a scale of 1-10 (10 being extremely important), rate how serious your most recent crisis is. Based on your score, assess whether you need to take action. If so, choose three problem-solving strategies to come up with a plan.

EXERCISE 49
Prioritize Daily Check-Ins

Self-care is often misunderstood as being a luxury nowadays. You may see photos of teens purchasing expensive clothes or the latest foods and drinks and captioning the post with **#self-care.**

The real definition of self-care is the ability to respond to your needs. On a basic level, this means being able to feed, clothe, and protect yourself. But on an advanced level, responding to your needs is about being able to sense when you are not physically or emotionally well and prioritizing your wellbeing.

Daily check-ins are short five minute breaks where you pause and assess your mental and emotional state. Three simple questions to ask yourself are: What am I thinking? What am I feeling? What do I need right now?

If you cannot immediately take action, write down your needs or concerns and schedule time later to address them. Don't let the day end before going back and responding to your needs.

Below is a table that you can use to log your daily check-ins:

Day of the week	How many check-ins did you have today?	What thoughts came up?	What feelings came up?	How did you respond to your needs?
Monday				
Tuesday				
Wednesday				
Thursday				
Friday				
Saturday				
Sunday				

EXERCISE 50
30-Day Self-Care Challenge

The best way to ensure that you prioritize self-care is to make time for yourself every day. Complete 30 days of self-care by participating in the following daily challenges:

Day	Challenge	Comments
1	Set positive intentions for the day.	
2	Limit social media usage to only 30 minutes daily.	
3	Schedule a 10-minute catch up with your parents.	
4	Plan a short-term goal.	
5	Clean your bedroom.	

Day	Challenge	Comments
6	Start a new hobby.	
7	Listen to a motivational podcast.	
8	Write a gratitude list.	
9	Go to bed early.	
10	Cook a healthy meal.	
11	Create a calming music playlist.	
12	Do a random act of kindness.	
13	Create a vision board.	
14	Spend time outdoors.	
15	Thank someone.	

Day	Challenge	Comments
16	Drink chamomile tea before bed.	
17	Set a reminder for three daily check-ins during the day.	
18	Start reading a new book.	
19	Complete a 30-minute cardio workout video.	
20	Eliminate unhealthy food or ingredients from your diet.	
21	Have a date with yourself.	
22	Video call a close friend.	
23	Create five positive affirmations to encourage yourself.	

Day	Challenge	Comments
24	Journal about something on your mind.	
25	Complete a 10-minute meditation.	
26	Try a new experience that is outside of your comfort zone.	
27	Create a face mask with kitchen ingredients and give yourself a facial.	
28	Watch funny videos on YouTube.	
29	Take a photo of something that makes you happy.	
30	Take a walk without your phone.	

Journal Prompts

Do you wish to learn more about building a healthy self-esteem? Here are some journal prompts that can help you think of more ways to confront your inner critic and overcome self-doubt. Take your time to respond thoughtfully to each prompt.

1. *What activities make you feel good about yourself?*

_____

_____

_____

_____

_____

2. *Who are the people within your social circle that bring out the best version of you?*

_____

_____

_____

_____

3. What is holding you back from expressing who you are unapologetically?

_____

_____

_____

_____

_____

4. If you could conquer the fear of failure, what decisions would you make about your life right now?

_____

_____

_____

_____

_____

_____

5. *How can you continue to improve your mental health?*

_____

_____

_____

_____

_____

6. *How can you become more intentional about practicing positive self-talk?*

_____

_____

_____

_____

_____

_____

7. *What do you need to accept about your life right now to feel better about it?*

_____

_____

_____

_____

_____

Conclusion

Avoid focusing on what you cannot do. Instead, focus on what you can do and accomplish without expecting approval and recognition from others.

Lisa Lieberman-Wang

When life gets tough, you need to get tougher. The purpose of learning coping skills, and practicing these exercises over and over again, is to prepare yourself mentally and emotionally for unexpected challenges and ongoing difficult situations you may encounter at home or at school.

Over time, you will notice the CBT and DBT skills you learn become second nature. Instead of turning to your usual defense mechanisms, your brain will respond with the appropriate coping skill.

Can you imagine the difference in your mood and behaviors when you are able to manage unwanted thoughts and identify the early signs of stress? Or when anxiety-triggering events no longer cause you to withdraw, overthink, isolate yourself, or do things you will later regret?

These are the positive outcomes you can look forward to when self-directed therapy becomes an integral part of your life!

These teenage years won't get any easier the older you get, but since you are equipped with the tools to confront and proactively solve your problems, you have everything you need to overcome whatever storms may come your way.

If you have enjoyed going through this workbook, please leave a review on Amazon.

Dear Reader,

Thank you for choosing to read my workbook. I sincerely hope it has provided you with valuable insights and practical guidance on your personal development journey. Your feedback is incredibly important to me.

If you found this book helpful or thought-provoking, I kindly request that you consider sharing your thoughts through a review. By doing so, you can help others discover the book and make an informed decision about whether it alights with their needs.

Leaving a review is quick and easy. You will just require your smartphone or tablet to scan the QR code below. This will take you to the review page for this workbook, and from there all you have to do is select a star rating, leave an honest review and click submit.

Your review will not only help me grow as an author but will also assist other individuals seeking guidance on their personal development journeys.

I appreciate your time and support. Thank you for being a part of this transformative experience.

Best regards,

Richard Bass.

About the Author

Richard Bass is a well-established author with extensive knowledge and background in children's disabilities. Richard has also experienced firsthand many children and teens who deal with depression and anxiety. He enjoys researching techniques and ideas to better serve students, as well as providing guidance to parents on how to understand and lead their children to success.

He wants to share his experience, research, and practices through his writing, as it has proven successful to many parents and students.

He feels there is a need for parents and others around the child to fully understand the disability or the mental health of the child. He hopes that with his writing people will be more understanding of children going through these issues.

He has been in education for over a decade and holds a bachelor's and master's degree in education, as well as several certifications including Special Education for K-12 and Educational Administration.

Whenever he is not working, reading, or writing, he likes to travel with his family to learn about different cultures, as well as get ideas from all around about the upbringing of children, especially those with disabilities. He also researches and learns about different educational systems around the world.

He participates in several online groups where parents, educators, doctors, and psychologists share their success about children with disabilities. He is in the process of growing a Facebook group where further discussion about his books and techniques could take place. Apart from online groups, he has also attended training regarding the upbringing of students with disabilities and led training in this area.

A Message from the Author

If you enjoyed the book and are interested on further updates or just a place to share your thoughts with other readers or myself, please join my Facebook group by scanning below!

If you would be interested on receiving a FREE Planner for kids PDF version, by signing up you will also receive exclusive notifications to when new content is released and will be able to receive it at a promotional price. Scan below to sign up!

Scan below to check out my content on You Tube and learn more about Neurodiversity!

References

American Psychiatric Association. (2019, January). What is psychotherapy? Psychiatry. https://www.psychiatry.org/patients-families/psychotherapy

Beard, C. (2021, June 23). How to set daily intentions. The Blissful Mind. https://theblissfulmind.com/daily-intentions/

Davis, T. (n.d.). What is reappraisal–and how do you do it? The Berkeley Wellbeing Institute. https://www.berkeleywellbeing.com/reappraisal.html

DBT skill: ACCEPTS (worksheet). (n.d.). Therapist Aid. https://www.therapistaid.com/therapy-worksheet/dbt-accepts

Define cognitive behavioral therapy. (n.d.). Cognitive Behavioral Therapy Los Angeles. https://cogbtherapy.com/define-cognitive-behavioral-therapy

Dialectical behavior therapy (DBT). (2022, April 19). Cleveland Clinic. https://my.clevelandclinic.org/health/treatments/22838-dialectical-behavior-therapy-dbt

Editors. (2022, September 30). 50 Questions to ask when requesting feedback from colleagues. Enlightio. https://enlightio.com/questions-to-ask-when-requesting-feedback-from-colleagues

Erstling, T. (2019, January 31). The personification of emotions. https://troyerstling.com/personification-emotions/

Gardner, E. (2022, April 30). How to utilize CBT for intrusive thoughts. Online Therapy. https://www.online-therapy.com/blog/how-to-utilize-cbt-for-intrusive-thoughts

Gilles, G. (2014, August 7). Being proactive about problem-solving-wellness, disease prevention, and stress reduction information. Mental Help. https://www.mentalhelp.net/blogs/being-proactive-about-problem-solving/

Harvard School of Public Health. (2020, September 14). Mindful eating. The Nutrition Source. https://www.hsph.harvard.edu/nutritionsource/mindful-eating/

The importance of nervous system regulation. (2022, April 29). Avalon Malibu. https://www.avalonmalibu.com/blog/the-importance-of-nervous-system-regulation/

Internal vs. external events. (n.d.). Dialectical Behavior Therapy. https://dialecticalbehaviortherapy.com/mindfulness/internal-vs-external-events

Invajy. (2023, March 25). 100 Inspiring self-esteem quotes to boost self-worth and self-love. Self-Improvement Blog. https://www.invajy.com/self-esteem-quotes/

Lockett, E. (2022, April 18). Can you be your own therapist? Why self-therapy may be for you. Psych Central. https://psychcentral.com/health/self-therapy#pros-of-self-therapy

Mental body scan. (n.d.). Dialectical Behavior Therapy. https://dialecticalbehaviortherapy.com/mindfulness/mental-body-scan/

Mikhail, A. (2023, March 8). 6 Million Americans have intrusive thoughts. Here are 4 ways to get rid of them. Yahoo Finance. https://finance.yahoo.com/news/6-million-americans-intrusive-thoughts-185601561.html

Miller, K. (2020, January 7). 28 Best therapy quotes and do they ring true? Positive Psychology. https://positivepsychology.com/best-therapy-quotes/

Negative emotions quotes (25 quotes). (n.d.). Good Reads. https://www.goodreads.com/quotes/tag/negative-emotions

Quotes about problem-solving. (2018). Great Expectations. https://www.greatexpectations.org/resources/life-principles/problem-solving/quotes-about-problem-solving/

Raising low self-esteem. (2021, February 1). NHS. https://www.nhs.uk/mental-health/self-help/tips-and-support/raise-low-self-esteem/

Raypole, C. (2019, January 25). DBT: Dialectical behavioral therapy skills, techniques, what it treats. Healthline. https://www.healthline.com/health/dbt

Sinclair, J. (2021, July 12). How mindful breathing can change your day (and your life). BetterUp. https://www.betterup.com/blog/mindful-breathing

60% of young people are unable to cope due to pressure to succeed. (2018, May 16). Mental Health Foundation. https://www.mentalhealth.org.uk/about-us/news/60-young-people-unable-cope-due-pressure-succeed

Smith, K. (2022, October 21). 6 Common triggers of teen stress. Psycom. https://www.psycom.net/common-triggers-teen-stress

Star, K. (2022, March 10). Visualization techniques can help manage your symptoms. Verywell Mind. https://www.verywellmind.com/visualization-for-relaxation-2584112

Sutton, J. (2020, June 19). Socratic questioning in psychology: Examples and techniques. Positive Psychology. https://positivepsychology.com/socratic-questioning/

Sutton, J. (2021, December 3). How to help clients express their feelings and emotions: 6 Worksheets. Positive Psychology. https://positivepsychology.com/express-feelings/

Teenage stress quotes, quotations, and sayings 2023. (n.d.). Search Quotes. https://www.searchquotes.com/search/Teenage_Stress/2/

Thought diffusion. (n.d.). Dialectical Behavior Therapy. https://dialecticalbehaviortherapy.com/mindfulness/thought-defusion/

Turkel, L. (2023, January 13). 37 Calm quotes that will bring you inner peace. Reader's Digest. https://www.rd.com/list/quotes-calm/

20 Problem-solving activities to improve creativity. (2019). Humor That Works. https://www.humorthatworks.com/how-to/20-problem-solving-activities-to-improve-creativity/

Vaughn, S. (2022, November 30). DBT emotion regulation skills: Emotion psychoeducation and mindfulness. Psychotherapy Academy. https://psychotherapyacademy.org/dbt/dbt-emotion-regulation-skills-emotion-psychoeducation-mindfulness/

What is cognitive behavioral therapy? (2017, July). American Psychological Association. https://www.apa.org/ptsd-guideline/patients-and-families/cognitive-behavioral

Wilson, F. (2019, November 29). Top 20 problem-solving activities for your team to master. NTask Manager Blog. https://www.ntaskmanager.com/blog/top-problem-solving-activities-for-your-team-to-master/

"Safe place" relaxation exercise. (2019, October 30). Spring Psychology. https://www.springpsychology.co.uk/post/safe-place-relaxation-exercise

Image References

Cameron, J. M. (2020a). [Boy in yellow crew neck t-shirt writing on white paper] [Image]. Pexels. https://www.pexels.com/photo/boy-in-yellow-crew-neck-t-shirt-writing-on-white-paper-4144173/

Cameron, J. M. (2020b). [Photo of girl writing on white paper] [Image]. Pexels. https://www.pexels.com/photo/photo-of-girl-writing-on-white-paper-4143794/

Grabowska, K. (2021). [Teenage girl sitting with headphones on holding a Coca-Cola can] [Image]. Pexels. https://www.pexels.com/photo/teeange-girl-sitting-with-headphones-on-holding-a-coca-cola-can-8005020/

Nilov, M. (2021). [A boy with head down leaning on a bookcase] [Image]. Pexels. https://www.pexels.com/photo/a-boy-with-head-down-leaning-on-a-bookcase-7929278/

Shvets Production. (2021). [Happy Black man resting in soft armchair] [Image]. Pexels. https://www.pexels.com/photo/happy-black-man-resting-in-soft-armchair-6974762/

Shvets, A. (2020). [Multi-ethnic teenagers on white background looking away] [Image]. Pexels. https://www.pexels.com/photo/multiethnic-teenagers-on-white-background-looking-away-5325742/

Zimmerman, P. (2020). [Therapist comforting patient] [Image]. Pexels. https://www.pexels.com/photo/therapist-comforting-patient-3958464/

Made in the USA
Monee, IL
08 April 2024

56602085R00092